What Else Can I 1
Flute
Grade Two

© International Music Publications Ltd

First published in 1995 by International Music Publications Ltd

International Music Publications Ltd is a Faber Music company

Bloomsbury House 74–77 Great Russell Street London WC1B 3DA

Series Editor: Mark Mumford

Cover designed by Lydia Merrills-Ashcroft

Music arranged and processed by Barnes Music Engraving Ltd

Printed in England by Caligraving Ltd

All rights reserved

ISBN10: 0-571-53051-6

EAN13: 978-0-571-53051-9

To buy Faber Music publications or to find out about the full range of titles available,
please contact your local music retailer or Faber Music sales enquiries:

Faber Music Ltd, Burnt Mill, Elizabeth Way, Harlow, CM20 2HX England

Tel: +44(0)1279 82 89 82   Fax: +44(0)1279 82 89 83

sales@fabermusic.com   fabermusic.com

Introduction

In this *What Else Can I Play?* collection you'll find sixteen popular tunes that are both challenging and entertaining.

The pieces have been carefully selected and arranged to create ideal supplementary material for young flautists who are either working towards or have recently taken a Grade Two flute examination.

Technical demands increase progressively, gradually introducing new concepts that reflect the requirements of the major examination boards. Each piece offers suggestions and guidelines on breathing, dynamics and tempo, together with technical tips and performance notes.

Pupils will experience a wide variety of music, ranging from folk and classical through to showtunes and popular songs, leading to a greater awareness of musical styles.

Whether it's for light relief from examination preparation, or to reinforce the understanding of new concepts, this collection will enthuse and encourage all young flute players.

Note: references to fingering within this book use Thumb 1 2 3 4.

Scarborough fair

Traditional

The sun has got his hat on

Words and Music by Ralph Butler and Noel Gay

The teddy bears' picnic

Words by Jimmy Kennedy, Music by John Bratton

Do-Re-Mi

Words by Oscar Hammerstein II, Music by Richard Rodgers

Miss Marple

Ken Howard and Alan Blaikley

Que sera, sera
(Whatever will be, will be)

Words and Music by Jay Livingston and Ray Evans

Last of the summer wine

Ronnie Hazlehurst

What shall we do with the drunken sailor?

Traditional

Green grow the rashes O'

Robert Burns

Mairzy doats and dozy doats

Words and Music by Milton Drake, Al Hoffman and Jerry Livingston

Gavotte

Giovanni Martini

The green leaves of summer

Words by Paul Francis Webster, Music by Dimitri Tiomkin

That's amore

Words by Jack Brooks, Music by Harry Warren

When the red, red robin comes bob, bob, bobbin' along

Words and Music by Harry Woods

The piper o' Dundee

Traditional

Wouldn't it be loverly

Words by Alan Jay Lerner, Music by Frederick Loewe

FLUTE VOLUMES

from Faber Music

76 Graded Studies for Flute. Book 1 *Sally Adams & Paul Harris*
ISBN 0-571-51430-8

76 Graded Studies for Flute. Book 2 *Sally Adams & Paul Harris*
ISBN 0-571-51431-6

Improve your sight-reading! Grades 1–3 *Paul Harris*
ISBN 0-571-51466-9

Improve your sight-reading! Grades 4–5 *Paul Harris*
ISBN 0-571-51467-7

Improve your sight-reading! Grade 6 *Paul Harris*
ISBN 0-571-51789-7

Improve your sight-reading! Grades 7–8 *Paul Harris*
ISBN 0-571-51790-0

Improve your scales! Grades 1–3 *Paul Harris*
ISBN 0-571-52024-3

Improve your scales! Grades 4–5 *Paul Harris*
ISBN 0-571-52025-1

First Repertoire for Flute *Sally Adams & Nigel Morley*
ISBN 0-571-52163-0

Concert Repertoire for Flute *Sally Adams & Nigel Morley*
ISBN 0-571-52164-9